This house b
Bangers and
A bell hangs

Mum is singing
as she dusts the house.

Bangers and Mash swing up
and ring the bell.
Ding, dong!

3

Then they run off
so Mum can't see them.

4

Mum opens the door.
She is cross.
Bangers and Mash
must have rung the bell.

5

Along comes the postman.
He is bringing a long box.

He swings up to the bell
and rings it.
Ding, dong!

Then he bangs on the door.

Mum stops dusting
and singing her song.
"Stop that ringing!"

She opens the door yelling,
"No pudding for you!"

Down falls the postman.
Bang on his head!

Dad is picking him up
and dusting him down.

12

In the long box is a swing
for Bangers and Mash.

Dad is fixing the swing up
in the tree.

14

Bangers is on the swing.
With a long swing up
he can just ring the bell!

15

As Mum gets to the door
Aunt Lill comes along
with her little baby, Bubble.

16

Mum can't be cross now.
She picks up Bubble
and gives her a cuddle.

"Come in
for a little, Lill,"
she says.

Bubble cries.
Bangers jumps down and
picks the baby's rattle up.

He rattles the rattle.
The baby stops crying
and chuckles.

20

He picks up Bubble's bottle
and has a drink.
Bubble just blows bubbles.

Next he picks up Bubble
and gives her a cuddle.
Bubble dribbles on him.

22

Mash comes up.
He tickles Bubble in the
middle of her little tummy.

Bangers puts Bubble back.
Bubble stops chuckling
and cries.

24

Bangers and Mash grab
the pram by the handle
and give it a big push.

It stops in the middle
of a puddle.
They stand in the puddle
up to their ankles.

They paddle up and down.
Bubble grins and dribbles.

Mum comes out
to give Bubble her bottle.

She sees the pram
in the middle of the puddle.

28

She runs up but sees that
Bubble is not crying
and is chuckling.

Mum goes back in and
brings out two big apples
for Bangers and Mash.

30

Aunt Lill comes for Bubble.
What a muddle in
the middle of the puddle!

Things to do

1 Add letters and make up words from the
  story.
  _angs   _angs   _ings   __ings
  _ong   _ung   sing__   bring__
  dust__   yell__   fix __

2 Add a letter and make up your own words.
  _ang   _ing   _ong   sung
  _atting   _itting   _opping   _inning
  _unning

3 Copy out these words. Underline the one
  with the different sound. (Work across.)
  bang   hang   ding   sang
  ring   fling   bring   sung
  long   strong   dong   sing
  lung   hung   rang   flung

4 Add letters and make up words from the
  story.
  _attle   _ittle   _ottle   _uddle
  ank__   midd__   tick__   mudd__